Poets Writing in a Variety of Forms

selected by Wes Magee

Contents

Raps
Haiku's

LONGMAN

A Poem to Emus

The problem with keeping some emus
Is telling which ones are the she 'mus
    They all have long legs,
    But, only one lays the eggs.
those that don't are obviously he 'mus.

David Whitehead

David Whitehead writes:

Limericks are jokey poems. Lines 1, 2 and 5 have the same rhyme, while lines 3 and 4 have a different rhyme. It is said such poems originated in Limerick, Ireland, where gatherings of people would amuse themselves by inventing the poems, each person contributing a different line. It was a poetic form famously used by Edward Lear.

I am a small iridescent twig,
Silver wrapped like a thin sweet.
A catch-sun, though you will not
    catch me,
Too quick as I skim the waters I
    came from.
When I pause on a reed or a lily's
    landing pad
I'm watching you as you marvel.
You look again: I've gone!

John Cotton

John Cotton writes:

Do you have favourite words? One of mine is "iridescent" which means glittering, flashing, the colours of the rainbow, like the effect you get from sunlight on crumpled silver paper. When I saw a dragonfly hovering and darting by a stream where I live I was reminded of those silver-paper wrapped sweets ... and the poem started.

Reflections in a Pond

A
tree
by a pond
reflected on
its annual crop of
gold
h f
s i
i s
f h
gold
its annual crop of
reflected on
by a pond
tree
A

Carol Coiffait

6

Carol Coiffait writes:

I spotted this poem one May when I was in the sun-house. There's a plum tree and a pond close by, and as I fed the goldfish they surfaced among reflections of leaves on the water. I thought: what strange fruit for a plum tree! And the shape poem was born ...

7

The River Cinquains

Morning
Moorland:
Purple heather.
Early sun lights the stream:
Rushing, chattering, swift with fish,
Sparkling.

Afternoon
Townscape:
Water reflects
Grey brickwork, dull windows.
Fishermen stare. The river moves
Slowly.

Evening

Salt-marsh:

Under lead skies

The water slides away

From the damp banks of sand a few

Birds call.

Nigel Cox

Nigel Cox writes:

Cinquains are five lines long
and offer the challenge of
syllable counting: 22
syllables in the sequence: 2,
4, 6, 8, 2. The way each line
grows in length suggested the
course of a river to me and
the sequence moves through
the hours of the day as well.
My favourite landscapes in
just fifteen lines!

Simple Seasons

Swallows,
Primroses
Return.
It's
New,
Green!

Skylarks
Up,
Meadows
Motley,
Elms
Regal.

Apples
Untold,
Trees
Unruly;
Mists
Now

Waters
Icebound,
Naked
Trees;
Earth
Rests.

Eric Finney

Eric Finney writes:

I began these acrostics by writing the four seasons (spring; summer; autumn; winter) down the page, and then thought of single words that were appropriate. It was a good test to try and create a language picture for each season in the minimum number of words.

from Dinner on Elm Street

Thrice the old school cat hath spewed.

Teachers shriek and children whine:

Ring the bell! 'Tis time! 'tis time!

Round about the cauldron go,

In the mouldy cabbage throw,

Stone-cold custard, thick with lumps,

Germs from Kevin (sick with mumps).

Boil up sprouts for greenish smell,

Add sweaty sock, cheese pie as well.

Here's the spell to make you thinner.

It's the nightmare Elm Street dinner.

Froth and splutter, boil and bubble,

March them in here at the double!

Michaela Morgan

Michaela Morgan writes:

This is a spell model in the
form of a spell
in Shakespeare's play
Macbeth. Instead of three
witches putting ingredients
into a cauldron my version
has three dinner ladies putting
in ingredients to make
nightmare school dinners – at
Elm Street Juniors. I use the
same form and rhythm as
Shakespeare, but change
some of the ingredients.

An A–Z of Bopping Birds

All
Birds
Can
Dance:
Eagles
Foxtrot and
Go-go!
Honest,
It's true!
Jays,
Kestrels and
Lapwings
Mambo!

Nightingales and

Owl

Pogo!

Quails and

Rooks

Shuffle and

Twist!

Unbelievable, isn't it!

Vultures

Waltz

Xtra-ordinarily well – and

Yellowhammers

Zigzag!

(okay, so I made that
   one up)

James Carter

James Carter writes:

I typed ABCD on to my computer and stared at the letters until "All Birds Can Dance" came to me. Then, I chose a bird ("E") and a dance ("F") and went on from there. I knew most of these bird names, others I found in my thesaurus.

Trevor Harvey writes:

The shape of a musical instrument is important for the sound it produces. I thought it would be fun if the names of the instruments could also make those shapes on the page. You can see that I've let the words grow in size as the volume of the music increases!

Rhythm Machine

Soft and

humming—

LOUD

and **strumming—**

Listen to the NEAT refrain!

Add a **TRUMPET**

Add a  kit–

Why not change the B
        E
          A
            T again?

UP THE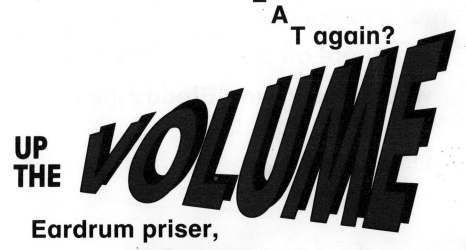

Eardrum priser,

 POPGROUP

SyntheSIZER!

Trevor Harvey

21

from Down There on the Corner

Down there on the corner
at the far end of the street
hear the chatter and the patter and the
sound of stamping feet
to a blaster that is pounding out
a really funky beat
  down there on the corner
    where The Young Bloods meet.

Down there on the corner
at the far end of the street
all the teenies and the weenies
do the high fives when they greet
while the music is coolly thumping
through the summer's dust and heat
down there on the corner
where The Young Bloods meet.

Wes Magee

Wes Magee writes:

If you read the poem aloud you will "hear" the toe-tapping rhythm. The musical beat is underlined by using the same rhyme sound throughout the poem – street/feet/beat/meet/street/greet/heat/meet. The last two lines in each verse act as a refrain or chorus.

Kestrel

Windhover, stretch-wing
high above motorway lanes
eyeing small carnages
swooping on crushed fur and flesh;
remember who may be next.

25

Searching

On the hard shoulder
silver and black veiled in dust
lies a dead badger
eyes glazed, nose crusted with blood;
ten car lengths on lies its mate.

Pat Leighton

Pat Leighton writes:

When I'm writing short image
poems such as Tanka or Haiku
I like to keep to what I've seen
or experienced. Words can't be
wasted, and thinking about
your feelings leads you to the
best ones. Descriptions may
be simple and must be true,
and if they're good the more
the reader should discover.

Dustbin Liner

The ghost of all our rubbish come
  to haunt us.
A ragged crow that blows about
  the garden.
A giant's burnt rice pudding skin.
Black ice waiting to be skidded on.
The shroud of many unimportant things.
A limbless, bulging belly.
A cauldron brewing garbage soup.
A witch's plastic mac.
The envelope from a long black letter.
The silent hungry beggar at my door.

Sue Cowling

Sue Cowling writes:

Examining an everyday object closely for the first time can be exciting, amusing or scary. I try to see it through the eyes of a visitor from another planet! You can write a list of ideas yourself (or as a group), then decide which order they should go in to make a poem.

Cricket Bat

DISMAL TES

SCORES

MAKE ME RATTY.

I'M A LITTLE

CRICKET BATTY

Jenny Morris

This is the Chimney

JENNY MORRIS

This is the chimney all askew. This is the roof that has a tilt. These are the walls the wind blows this is the through house that Jerry built.

Jenny Morris

Jenny Morris writes:

My shape poems start from doodles. I draw an outline, then think of some line to fit the subject. Making the letters large or small is enjoyable, a sort of improvisation. "Cricket Bat" concerns a passion for the game which borders on eccentricity. "This is the Chimney" is about a draughty, old house where I once lived.

In the Kitchen

In the kitchen
After the aimless
Chatter of the plates,
The murmurings of the gas,
The chuckle of the water pipes
And the sharp exchanges
Of the knives, forks and spoons,
Comes the serious quiet,
When the sink slowly clears its throat
And you can hear the occasional rumble
Of the refrigerator's tummy
As it digests the cold.

John Cotton

John Cotton writes:

Do you, like me, listen to the silence? You can hear all those small noises that get drowned out in the rush of the day. You listen with your imagination, of course. I listened to my kitchen one night and I imagined the conversation that was going on between the plates, the knives, the gas stove and the sink.

Lost: One Dragon

Loving pet

escaped from the vet.

Wings: jointed. Scales: shiny.

Tail: pointed. Brain: tiny.

Length: one mile: Happy smile.

Teeth like a crocodile.

Maybe carrying a shield and sword.

Please call George.

Generous reward.

Celia Warren

Celia Warren writes:

I enjoy the conciseness of small ads. When you pay by the word, every word has to earn its keep. Each word in a poem has to work hard too. My advert poem grew from the thought "What if ...?", then some rhyming words crept in. And the fun began.

Well, You Shouldn't Have ...

"Er, Mum – I've just had an explosion."

"Well, you shouldn't have shaken
your drink!"

"Er, Mum – I've just flooded
the bathroom."

"Well, you shouldn't have blocked
up the sink!"

"Er, Mum – I've just spilt Grandad's
maggots."

"Well, you shouldn't have been in
his shed!"

"Er, Mum – I've just tidied my bedroom."
"Well, you shouldn't have ...
    WHAT'S that you said?"

Sue Cowling

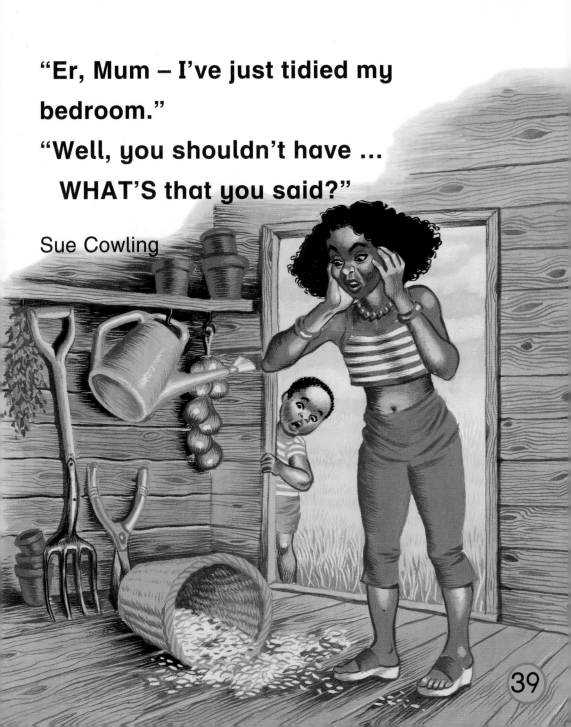

Sue Cowling writes:

All mums have their little catchphrases – I was caught out by mine and decided to laugh at myself in a poem. It wasn't hard to think of exasperating things my own children, or myself, had done! Using two different voices can be a useful way of bringing out the conflict in a situation.

Thursday, 6th November

Last night, bad dreams

in the back bedroom

although bangers

and rockets have stopped.

Drum-rolls of wind

on the window's skin

and slung hail like dried peas

... bop bop bop ...

Carol Coiffait

Carol Coiffait writes:

I keep a writer's notebook, a sort of diary. When I looked back to November 1997 I realised why I had bad dreams and restless nights – my mother was about to have an operation. I was able to make a diary verse from one entry.

Elephantasia

If an elephant wore big rubber boots –
   Would it be a Wellyphant?

Or if one was raspberry red and wobbly –
   Would it be a Jellyphant?

If you saw one on a TV show –
   Would it be a Telephant?

What if an elephant never had a shower –
   Would he be a Smellyphant?

Or if one go so very, very fat –
   Might we say – Pot-bellyphant?

Do you think we'll ever, ever know?
   No, not on your Nelly-phant!

David Whitehead

David Whitehead writes:

Absurd or ridiculous verse is known as nonsense poetry. Even so, it still needs rhythm and rhyme. Lewis Carroll's "Jabberwocky" is a great nonsense poem. When I wrote "Elephantasia" I thought of all the words that had "ele" in them, and then posed questions.

from Superstar

I WANNA BE A SUPERSTAR.

I wanna drive a massive car.

I wanna join the famous set.

I wanna own a private jet.

I wanna lotta fun at nights.

I wanna name that's up in lights.

I wanna lotta caviar.

I WANNA BE A SUPERSTAR.

I wanna wear a lamé suit.

I wanna be a hunky brute.

I wanna song at number one.

I wanna headline in The Sun.

I wanna be like you-know-who.

I wanna be on TV too.

I wanna thrash a flash guitar.

I WANNA BE A SUPERSTAR.

Charles Thomson

Charles Thomson writes:

I wanted to write a "modern" poem to use in my Poetry Shows in schools. I found the word "Superstar" at the end of a poem I read (by Kit Wright, I think) and that sparked off the idea. The refrain – "I WANNA BE A SUPERSTAR" – is shouted by certain children while the rest ("fans") clap, cheer and whistle.

The Night Sky Kennings

Bedroom bulb,
   tarnish spoon,
toenail clipping,
   wrinkled prune,
polished coin
   ... the moon,
   the moon.

Glitter scatter,
   dust from Mars,
seaside lights,
   quartz quasars,
spill of pearls
   ... the stars,
   the stars.

Wes Magee

Wes Magee writes:

Kennings are rather like short riddles. Each phrase (e.g. "glitter scatter") represents the subject (the stars) in a descriptive way. Long ago the Anglo-Saxon poets often used kennings in their poems. "Oar-steed" was a ship, and "bone-house" was a burial chamber.